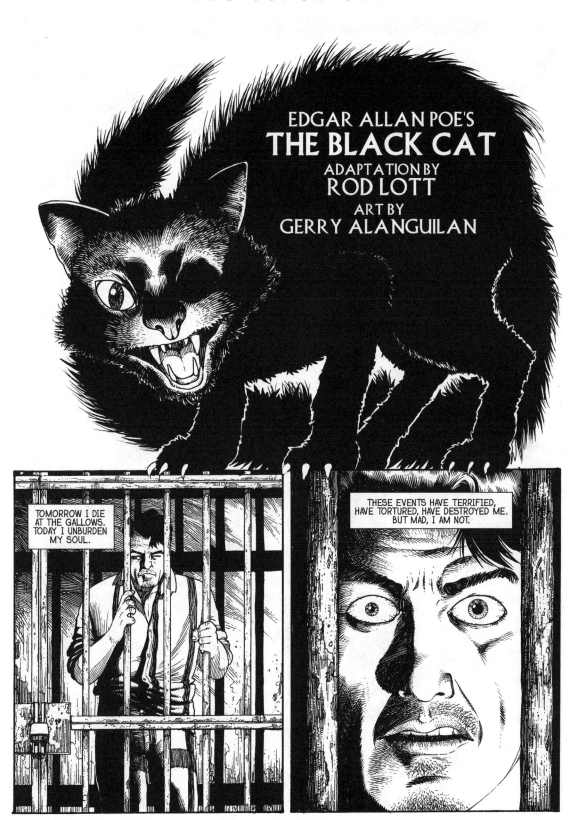

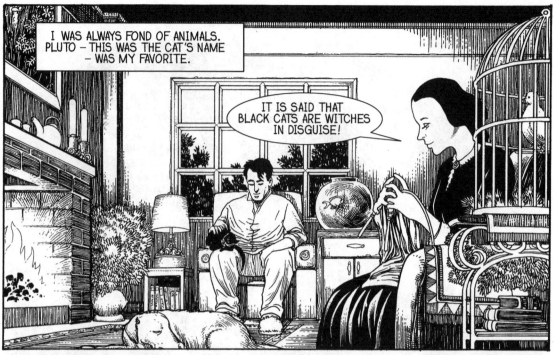

I WAS ALWAYS FOND OF ANIMALS. PLUTO – THIS WAS THE CAT'S NAME – WAS MY FAVORITE.

IT IS SAID THAT BLACK CATS ARE WITCHES IN DISGUISE!

HE ATTENDED ME WHEREVER I WENT.

OUR FRIENDSHIP LASTED FOR SEVERAL YEARS, UNTIL MY GENERAL TEMPERAMENT EXPERIENCED A RADICAL ALTERATION...

...FOR WHAT DISEASE IS ALCOHOL!

YELP!

IN THE MORNING, I FELT HORROR AND REMORSE FOR THE CRIME OF WHICH I WAS GUILTY...

I SOON DROWNED IN WINE ALL MEMORY OF THE DEED.

HE WAS OUTSIDE, AND GOT IN A TERRIBLE CAT FIGHT.

...AND, AS MIGHT BE EXPECTED, FLED IN TERROR AT MY APPROACH.

THE SOCKET PRESENTED A FRIGHTFUL APPEARANCE, BUT HE NO LONGER APPEARED TO SUFFER ANY PAIN...

THAT NIGHT...

FIRE!

MY ENTIRE WORLDLY WEALTH WAS SWALLOWED UP. I RESIGNED MYSELF HENCEFORWARD TO DESPAIR!

MY WIFE WAS OVERJOYED...

...BUT I SOON FOUND A DISLIKE TO THE ANIMAL RISING WITHIN ME.

ITS EYE!!

THE IMAGE OF THE GALLOWS! OF AGONY AND DEATH!

NOW I WAS WRETCHED BEYOND WRETCHEDNESS.

THE CAT'S PARTIALITY SEEMED TO INCREASE, EVEN AS MY DREAD OF THE BEAST GREW.

HERE AT LEAST, MY LABOR HAD NOT BEEN IN VAIN.

I SOUNDLY SLEPT, EVEN WITH THE BURDEN OF MURDER ON MY SOUL.

UPON THE FOURTH DAY, THE POLICE CAME TO MAKE A RIGOROUS INVESTIGATION OF THE PREMISES.

I DELIGHT IN ALLAYING YOUR SUSPICIONS, GENTLEMEN.

THIS IS A WELL-CONSTRUCTED HOUSE. THESE WALLS ARE SOLID.

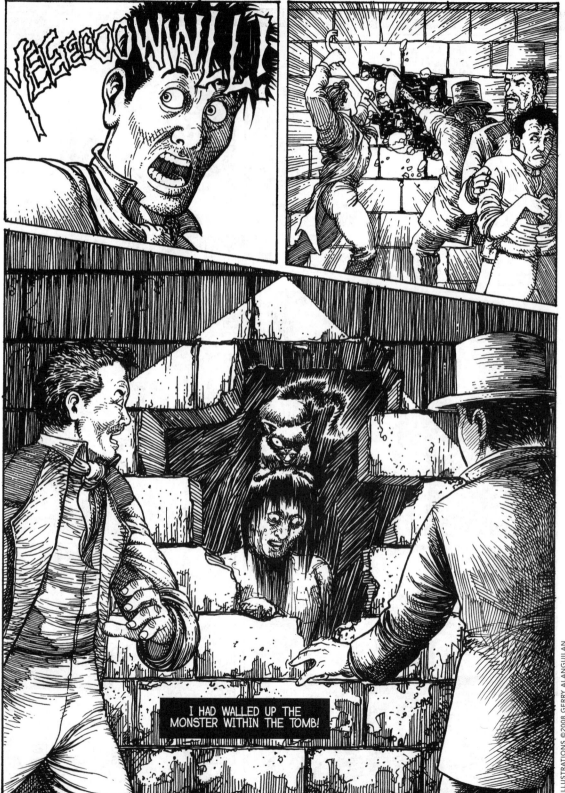

FOR MORE POE TALES SEE **HORROR CLASSICS**, **GOTHIC CLASSICS**, AND **GRAPHIC CLASSICS: EDGAR ALLAN POE**.

Arthur Conan Doyle's

JOHN BARRINGTON COWLES

Adaptation by Alex Burrows
Illustrated by Simon Gane

I met Barrington Cowles when I went to Edinburgh University to take medical classes. We originated a friendship unmarred by the slightest disagreement until the day of his death.

Even when a deeper passion came upon him, it never infringed on the tenderness between us. I recollect the first time we met her – it was at the Royal Scottish Academy…

I noticed an extremely beautiful woman standing at the other side of the room.

In my whole life I have never seen such a classically perfect countenance.

The more I looked at her the more her beauty grew upon me.

14

There was a young man with this lady whom I recognized as a law student with whom I had a slight acquaintance. He was a handsome young fellow named Archibald Reeves – a ringleader in every university escapade.

As the woman surveyed the room, I saw her gaze suddenly become fixed and intense.

Cowles' profile was turned towards us, and never have I seen him to such advantage.

It was evident that he had momentarily forgotten his surroundings, He came out of his reverie with a start and turned abruptly...

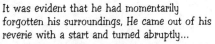

For several days he made no allusion to the subject, though my companion was perhaps a little more distracted than usual. Then one day I ran into young Brodie, a second cousin of mine.

I SAY, DID YOU KNOW REEVES' ENGAGEMENT IS OFF?

OFF?

DEUCEDLY MEAN OF REEVES —LEAVING KATE IN THE LURCH—ESPECIALLY AFTER WHAT HAPPENED TO HER PREVIOUS FIANCÉ!

KATE....?

KATE NORTHCOTT.

AND WHAT OF HER PREVIOUS FIANCÉ?

NO ONE REALLY KNOWS...

.....CALLED LATE ONE EVENING AT KATE'S, THEN THREE DAYS LATER HIS BODY WAS FOUND FLOATING IN THE LOCH.

RULED A SUICIDE— TEMPORARY INSANITY THEY SAY.

VERY STRANGE.

18

One cold night, several months after the conversation with Brodie, I was on my way back from a case. It was very late.

EVENIN', BORRB...

I recognized the degraded creature before me. There was no mistaking those features, which, although bloated with drink, still retained something of their former comeliness.

COME ALONG WITH ME — I'M GOING IN YOUR DIRECTION.

REEVES... REEVES IS THAT *YOU?*

He took my arm and I managed to get him back to his lodgings.

HIS PULSE IS SKY-HIGH! FEVERISH TOO...

19

Having seen that he would be properly cared for, I left the house. Reeves' words, however, rang in my ears for days after. When the winter session came on, I received a telegram from Barrington Cowles asking me to secure his old rooms.

BY THE WAY, YOU HAVE NOT CONGRATULATED ME YET.

ON WHAT, MY BOY?

WHAT! YOU HAVEN'T HEARD OF MY ENGAGEMENT?

ENGAGEMENT? NO! CONGRATULATIONS, JACK! WHO IS THE LUCKY LADY?

YOU REMEMBER THAT GIRL AT THE ACADEMY...

WHAT! YOU DON'T MEAN TO SAY YOU ARE ENGAGED TO HER?

OUR FAMILIES HAVE MUTUAL FRIENDS...

I MET HER DURING THE SUMMER... THE MORE I SEE KATE, THE MORE I LOVE HER.

YOU MUST BE INTRODUCED.

YES... YES, I MUST...

I expressed my pleasure at the prospect, but I felt anxious at heart. I went round with my friend a few days afterwards to call upon Miss Northcott.

THAT IS YOUR PROTOTYPE IN YOUR FAMILY, MISS NORTHCOTT.

DO YOU THINK SO? UNCLE ANTHONY WAS THE BLACK SHEEP OF THE FAMILY — BUT I THINK HE WAS WORTH MORE THAN ALL OF THEM.

HE WAS A RESPECTED OFFICER IN THE 41ST REGIMENT, AND DIED NOBLY FIGHTING IN THE PERSIAN WAR.

I WISH I'D BEEN A SOLDIER LIKE MY FATHER INSTEAD OF GOING INTO MEDICINE.

THAT'S THE SORT OF DEATH I SHOULD LIKE!

OH JACK! YOU ARE NOT GOING TO DIE ANY SORT OF DEATH YET.

That night I thought over all that I had seen and heard. My recollections were unpleasant, but there was no tangible charge I could bring against the woman.

How could I get at some conclusion to her real character and antecedents? Suddenly an idea struck me...

Among my father's friends was a Colonel Joyce who had served a long time in India, and who would be likely to know most of the officers out there. I proceeded to write him a letter about Captain Northcott...

I posted it, then retired to bed with a mind too anxious to allow me to sleep. I got an answer from Colonel Joyce in two days...

a gallant soldier enough, he distinguis Sobraon, and was wounded, if I remember not popular with his corps – they said he w cold-blooded fellow, with no geniality.. him. There was a rumor, too, th was a devil-worshippe also that he h was a

-blooded fellow, with... m. There was a rumor, too, that he had the evil eye, which, of course, a devil-worshipper and also that all nonsense. He had some strange about the power of the human will d the effects of mind upon matter.

P.S. By the way, Northcott did not fall in action. He was killed in a crazy attempt to get some of the eternal fire from the sun-worshippers' temple. There was considerable mystery about his death.

I read this epistle over several times. He was rumored to have the power of the evil eye. I could believe his niece's eyes, when endowed with that cold grey shimmer which I had noticed in them, were capable of great evil.

Could Miss Northcott, by relation, be endowed with some exceptional power? The idea grew on me...

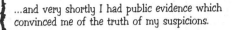

...and very shortly I had public evidence which convinced me of the truth of my suspicions.

I'VE NEVER SEEN A MESMERIST BEFORE, BOB. WHAT EXACTLY DO THEY DO?

MIND OVER MATTER, APPARENTLY. WE'LL SEE...

HEY, LOOK— COWLES AND HIS FIANCÉ ARE IN THE STALLS. HO! *JACK OLD BOY!*

SHHH! HE'S COMING ON!

The lecture and exhibition was somewhat commonplace until he came to the end...

I WOULD LIKE TO CONCLUDE THIS EVENING'S PERFORMANCE WITH A DEMONSTRATION OF MENTAL POWER...

DR. MESSINGER MESMERIST AND MEDIUM

BY THE MERE POWER OF *WILL* I SHALL SINGLE OUT A MEMBER OF THE AUDIENCE AND *COMPEL* HIM TO COME UP ON STAGE AND FOLLOW MY INSTRUCTIONS...

YOU DID THAT.

DID *WHAT*, MR. ARMITAGE?

YOU... *MESMERISED* THE MESMERISER.

I SEE. YOU CREDIT ME WITH A STRONG WILL?

A *DANGEROUSLY* STRONG ONE. ANY WILL WHICH CAN EXERCISE SUCH POWER IS DANGEROUS... IF IT WAS USED FOR *EVIL*.

I KNOW YOU ARE SUSPICIOUS OF ME, MR. ARMITAGE, THOUGH I HAVE NEVER GIVEN YOU CAUSE.

I'M JUST LOOKING AFTER MY FRIEND JACK.

30

And now I come to the beginning of the end. It was late that winter when Cowles remarked to me that he intended to marry Miss Northcott as soon as possible.

I'VE HAD A NOTE FROM KATE — ASKING ME TO CALL AT 11 O'CLOCK — AFTER MRS. MERTON RETIRES. DON'T WAIT UP, OLD CHAP!

I recalled the mysterious interview which preceded the death of Kate's former fiancé and the ravings of poor Reeves. What was the meaning of it all? Had this woman some baleful secret which must be disclosed before her marriage?

It was nearly 1 o'clock when I heard a step in the street outside, then a fumbling at the door...

BOB... HELP ME, BOB...

SHE IS A *FIEND*, BOB! A *GHOUL* FROM THE *PIT!* A VAMPIRE SOUL BEHIND A LOVELY FACE!

TRY TO SLEEP NOW. YOU HAVE A HIGH FEVER.

...*ANYTHING* IS BETTER THAN *THAT*... *DEATH* IS BETTER...

For weeks he lingered between life and death. But his vigorous constitution finally got the better of his disease. I nursed him during this anxious time; but he never let a word escape which explained the mystery of Miss Northcott.

THE ISLE OF MAY, JACK. JUST WHAT YOU NEED – FRESH SEA AIR AND LONG WALKS.

Cowles' severe illness had emaciated him greatly. His manner was eccentric and variable – sometimes irritable, sometimes recklessly mirthful, but never natural. This grim spot seemed to have a fascination for him, so we engaged a room in one of the fishermen's huts.

One night – our third on the island – Cowles and I stepped outside before retiring to rest, to enjoy a little fresh air.

The fishermen and I walked around the island all that night and examined every nook and corner without finding any trace of my friend.

The direction in which he had been running terminated in a rugged line of jagged cliffs overhanging the sea.

At one place the edge was somewhat crumbled, and there appeared marks upon the turf...

As we peered over the cliff, suddenly, above the beating of the waves and the howling of the wind, there rose a strange wild screech from the abyss below.

THAT'S A **WOMAN'S** LAUGHTER.

AYE, A **SEA SIREN**. TIME TO GO.

The superstitious fishermen could not be persuaded to continue the search. For my own part I think it must have been the cry of some sea-fowl startled from its nest.

However that may be, I do not want to hear such a sound again.

I have never seen Miss Northcott since, nor do I wish to do so. If by the words I have written I can save one human being from the snare of those bright eyes and that beautiful face, then I can lay down my pen with the assurance that my poor friend has not died altogether in vain.

THE END

ILLUSTRATIONS ©2008 SIMON GANE

MORE DOYLE TALES APPEAR IN **ADVENTURE CLASSICS** AND **GRAPHIC CLASSICS: ARTHUR CONAN DOYLE**.

The **Dream** by **Mary Shelley**.

Script by **Antonella Caputo**. Art by **Anne Timmons**.

The time of the occurrence of the little legend to be narrated was that of the commencement of the reign of Henry IV of France, whose accession and conversion were inadequate to heal the deep injuries mutually inflicted by the inimical parties.

Many of the fiercer Catholics retreated to their provinces, where they concealed in solitude their rankling discontent. In a large and fortified chateau overlooking the Loire dwelt the last of her race, and the heiress of their fortunes....

...the young and beautiful Constance, Countess de Villeneuve.

She had spent a year in solitude in her secluded abode. Her mourning for a father and two brothers, victims of the civil war, was a graceful reason why she didn't appear at court.

It was soon signified to her that the King, her guardian, desired that she should bestow her properties, together with her hand, upon a noble whose birth and accomplishments should entitle him to the gift.

DOMAINE du Count de VILLENEUVE

In reply she expressed her intention of taking vows and retiring to a convent.

The King forbade this act, believing the idea to be the result of sensibility overwrought by sorrow…

…and hoping that the spirit of youth would break through this cloud.

Another year passed, and still the countess persisted.

Henry announced his intention of visiting her chateau, desirous of judging for himself the motives that led one so beautiful and young to desire to bury herself in cloister.

In fact, Constance battled to cast off her grief. But she found she could best support the burden of her sorrow when, yielding to it, it oppressed but did not torture her.

Constance often left the castle to wander in the neighboring grounds. She felt pent up within the walls of her abode. The ancient woods held dear recollections of her past life, and enticed her to spend many hours beneath their leafy boughs.

The sun rained its beams through the boughs, soothing and calling her out of that dull sorrow which clutched her heart.

There was one nook of ground – a spot which she had forsworn – where she had unaware found herself.

Constance looked wistfully on the flowers she had herself planted to adorn the verdurous recess – to her the temple of memory and love.

She held the letter from the king, which was the parent of so much despair.

I BUT ASK TO LIVE IN MY FATHER'S HALLS, AND TO WATER WITH MY FREQUENT TEARS THE GRAVES OF THOSE I LOVED.

A rustling amongst the boughs now met her ear – her heart beat quick – then all again was still.

FOOLISH GIRL! DUPE OF THINE OWN PASSIONATE FANCY: BECAUSE HERE WE MET, NOW EVERY SOUND SPEAKS OF HIM.

OH GASPAR! NEVER AGAIN WILL THIS BELOVED SPOT BE MADE GLAD BY THEE!

KRACK!

Her first impulse was to fly…

…but once again to see him – to hear his voice – could not injure the dead, and would soften the sorrow that made her cheek so pale.

And now he was before her, the same beloved one with whom she had exchanged vows of constancy. Nor could she resist the imploring glance that entreated her to remain.

SPEAK NOT OF LOVE, GASPAR! A *SEA OF BLOOD* DIVIDES US *FOREVER!*

THE *DEAD* STAND BETWEEN US: THEIR PALE SHADOWS *MENACE* ME FOR LISTENING TO THEIR *MURDERER!*

THAT I AM *NOT!*

WHEN FIRST WE LOVED, MY OWN *MOTHER* BREATHED CURSES ON THE *HOUSE OF VILLENEUVE.* AND IN *SPITE* OF ALL I SAW *THEE,* MY LOVELY ONE, AND *BLESSED* IT...

"The god of peace planted love in our hearts, and in secrecy we met during many a summer night, and here we both knelt and made our vows. Shall they be broken?"

WAS IT FOR *US* TO TALK OF LOVE...

...WHEN *WAR* AND *HATE* AND *BLOOD* WERE RAGING ALL AROUND?

"By your father's hand, mine died..."

41

"You deny your **hand** dealt the blow that destroyed him, but you fought **among** those by whom he **died!**"

GO, GASPAR; *FORGET* ME. UNDER THE GALLANT HENRY YOUR CAREER MAY BE *GLORIOUS...*

...AND SOME GIRL WILL *LISTEN* TO YOUR VOWS AND BE MADE *HAPPY* BY THEM.

IN MY CLOISTER-HOME I SHALL NOT FORGET THE BEST CHRISTIAN LESSON — TO *PRAY* FOR ONE'S *ENEMIES.* GASPAR, FAREWELL!

Once within the seclusion of her apartment, she gave way to the burst of grief that tore at her gentle bosom like a tempest. Suddenly, a thought darted into her mind...

MANON... DIDST THOU EVER SLEEP ON *ST. CATHERINE'S COUCH?*

HEAVEN FORFEND! NONE *EVER* DID SINCE I WAS *BORN!* IT IS AN *AWFUL PLACE;* AND IF THE VOTARY HAS NOT LED A *PIOUS LIFE, WOE* BETIDE THE HOUR WHEN SHE RESTS HER HEAD ON THE HOLY STONE!

I WILL SLEEP ON THAT COUCH TOMORROW NIGHT!

MY DEAR LADY! AND THE *KING* ARRIVES TOMORROW!

THE MORE NEED THAT I RESOLVE. IT CANNOT BE THAT MISERY SO INTENSE SHOULD DWELL IN ANY HEART AND NO CURE BE FOUND.

I *WILL* REST TOMORROW NIGHT ON ST. CATHERINE'S BED, AND IF...

...AS I HAVE HEARD, THE SAINT DEIGNS DIRECT HER VOTARIES IN *DREAMS,* I WILL BE GUIDED BY HER, AND ACT ACCORDING TO THE DICTATES OF HEAVEN!

The King was on his way to Nantes, and he slept this night at a castle but a few miles distant. Before dawn, the young cavalier was admitted into his chamber.

SO THOU FOUNDEST HER OBDURATE, GASPAR?

ALAS! I FOUND HER RESOLVED IN OUR MUTUAL MISERY. I FEAR SHE WILL RESIST EVEN YOUR MAJESTY'S COMMANDS.

SHE IS BENT UPON ENTERING A CLOISTER; AND I, SO PLEASE YOU, WILL NOW TAKE MY LEAVE: I AM HENCEFORTH A *SOLDIER OF THE CROSS.*

LET THE VOICE OF THE WORLD REACH HER; AND BY *MY SAY* AND THE *HOLY CROSS* SHE WILL BE *YOURS.* LET OUR *PLAN* STILL HOLD.

GASPAR, I KNOW WOMAN BETTER THAN THOU. THE DEATH OF HER RELATIVES SITS HEAVY ON HER HEART. SHE FANCIES THAT HEAVEN ITSELF FORBIDS YOUR UNION!

AND NOW *TO HORSE:* THE MORNING *WEARS,* AND THE *SUN* IS RISEN!

43

In his disguise the cavalier viewed the calm countenance of the lady. Was this she whom he had seen trembling and weeping the evening before?

WHAT HO, MY FAITHFUL SERVING-MAN! COME *FORWARD*, AND *THANK* YOUR LADY FOR HER LOVE!

The King's call was in unison with Gaspar's impatience, and he sprang forward.

Overwrought by the very calmness she had assumed, Constance uttered a cry and sank senseless to the floor.

OOOOOHHHHHHH!

All this was very unintelligible. Even when her attendants had brought her to life, a flood of tears succeeded. The monarch knew not how to reply to Vaudemont's look of anxiety.

THE LADY IS ILL, MY LORD... TOMORROW SHE WILL SOLICIT YOUR PARDON AND DISCLOSE HER PURPOSE.

TOMORROW! AGAIN *TOMORROW!* CAN *YOU* NOT READ US THE RIDDLE, PRETTY ONE? WHAT STRANGE TALE BELONGS TO TOMORROW, THAT ALL RESTS UPON ITS ADVENT?

Henry was no tyro in the art of enticing ladies' attendants to disclose their intimacies.

Manon was frightened by the Countess' scheme, so she was more readily induced to betray it.

Could Constance, whom Henry had heard praised for her strength of mind, be so strangely infatuated?...

To sleep in *St. Catherine's Bed,* a narrow ledge overhanging the deep rapid Loire, to take the disturbed vision – *if* she escaped falling – *that* was a madness of which even Henry could scarcely deem *any* woman capable...

And can *passion* play such freaks with us – like death, bringing noble and peasant, the wise and the foolish under one thraldom? It was strange, yet she must have her way...

...but to the more *material* danger some safeguard could be brought.

In her own chamber, Constance awaited the night in an agony of anticipation.

There is no feeling more awful than that which invades a weak human heart bent upon gratifying its ungovernable impulses in contradiction to the dictates of *conscience*.

Softer and sweeter was the spirit of Constance, and *love* and *duty* contending crushed and tortured her poor heart.

To commit her conduct to the inspiration of religion, or if it was so to be named, of superstition, was a blessed relief. To dare for *his* sake was happiness.

Or if it was decreed that she must sacrifice *all,* the risk of death was of trifling import in comparison with the anguish which would then be her portion *forever.*

The night threatened to be stormy. Constance and Manon quitted the chateau and began to descend the hillside. Manon trembled; while the Countess walked with firm step down the steep.

They boarded a small boat and in but a few moments they were in the middle of the stream. The warm, tempestuous wind swept over them.

For the first time since her mourning, a thrill of pleasure swelled the bosom of Constance. She hailed the emotion with double joy…

"It cannot be that Heaven will forbid me to love one so good as the noble Gaspar!"

*"Oh no, life speaks aloud: I shall **live** to love!"*

*"Do not **all** things love? Heaven and earth are sustained by, and live through, love; and shall I alone be compelled to lock my heart forever?"*

These thoughts bade fair for pleasant dreams; but as thus she was engrossed by soft emotion, Manon caught her arm.

LADY, LOOK! IT COMES, YET THE OARS HAVE NOT SOUND! MAY THE VIRGIN SHIELD US!

GASPAR!?

A dark boat glided by them; four rowers and another at the helm…

…And though his face was turned from them, Constance recognized her lover.

GASPAR… DOST THOU LIVE?

But the figure in the boat neither turned it head nor replied and quickly was lost in the shadowy waters.

How changed was the fair Countess' reverie! Heaven had begun its spell. Now it seemed that another bark was there, which held the spirits of the dead; and her father waved to her, and her brothers frowned on her.

Her bark was moored in a little cove. Constance half-yielded to Manon's entreaty to return, until the unwise servant mentioned the King's name and the answer to be given tomorrow.

WHAT ANSWER, IF I TURNED BACK FROM MY INTENT?

Constance hurried forward up the ground of the bank, toward a small chapel which stood on the cliff.

The two women knelt and prayed. Then, rising, the countess bade her attendant goodnight as she unlocked a low iron door.

THOU MAYEST NOT FOLLOW, MY POOR MANON: THIS ADVENTURE IS FOR ME ALONE!

It seemed hardly fair to leave the trembling servant in the chapel alone, but Manon was safe on holy ground.

The countess pursued her way. At length she reached an open cavern looking over the rushing tide beneath.

Constance shuddered as she looked upon her bed: a narrow ledge of earth on the very edge of the precipice.

She doffed her mantle – such was one of the conditions of the spell – loosened her tresses and bared her feet…

…and fully prepared for suffering to the utmost the chill influence of the night, she stretched herself on the narrow couch.

If she moved in her sleep, she would tumble into the cold waters below!

What dreams would the saint send…

…to drive her to despair or to bid her be blessed forever?

Beneath the rugged hill, another watched, who feared and scarce dared hope.

What a vigil did the lovers keep! Love for him had led her to this perilous couch. She was alive only to a small still voice that whispered to her heart the dream which was to decide their destinies.

She slept perhaps, but he watched as the night wore away, his eyes fixed on the white garb of the slumberer above.

Would morning come to waken her? And what dreams peopled her sleep?

Gaspar grew impatient. He sprang forward intent upon climbing the precipice.

He clung to the rugged face of the hill, and found footing where it seemed no footing was.

Up the steep ascent Gaspar continued to toil and at last reached the root of a tree that grew near the summit.

Aided by the tree's branches, Gaspar made his stand at the very extremity of the edge, near the pillow on which lay the head of his beloved. Her face was serene. No statue hewn of marble was ever half so fair!

With what deep passion did Gaspar gaze, gathering hope from the placidity of her angelic countenance.

NO! HE SHALL **NOT** DIE;
I WILL **UNLOOSE** HIS CHAINS!
I WILL **SAVE** HIM!

Gaspar's hand was there. He caught her light form before it could fall from the perilous couch.

Constance opened her eyes and beheld her lover, who had watched over her dream of fate and who had saved her.

Manon also had slept well, and was startled in the morning to find that she waked surrounded by a crowd.

Manon saw that King Henry was there, but she looked for another whom she found not.

Then the iron door of the cavern passage opened and…

…Gaspar de Vaudemont entered, leading the fair form of Constance.

With deep emotion they approached the altar and pronounced the vows that united them forever.

It was long before the happy Gaspar could win from his lady the secret of her dream.

MANY A VISION I HAD THAT FEARFUL NIGHT!...

She had beheld Gaspar at King Henry's court, favored and beloved…

…and herself in a cloister weeping away her sad days – 'til suddenly…

The saint herself, Saint Catherine, guided her to a dark cell.

On the floor lay a man in tattered garments, his form a mere skeleton.

AND WAS IT MY APPEARANCE IN THAT ATTRACTIVE STATE THAT SOFTENED THE HARD HEART OF CONSTANCE?

EVEN SO, FOR MY HEART WHISPERED TO ME THAT THIS WAS *MY* DOING.

"A veil fell from my eyes; I knew for the first time what life and death was. You should *not* die; I would *loose* your chain and save you!"

I SPRANG FORWARD, BUT YOUR ARM WAS THERE TO SAVE *ME*, AND YOUR DEAR VOICE TO BID ME BE BLESSED FOR EVERMORE!

The End

MARY SHELLEY'S FAMED NOVEL **FRANKENSTEIN** IS PRESENTED IN **FANTASY CLASSICS**.

THINGS SEEMED WORSE UP THERE THAN THEY DID IN THE CAVERN, AND THE FURTHER THEY GOT ON THEIR WAY TO THE OUTSKIRTS, THE WORSE IT GOT.

ALL BEING READY, THE MAGICIAN OPENED THE CASKET AND LET THE FLESHY THING FALL IN TO BOIL.

LORD DUNSANY'S POEM **AFTER THE FIRE** IS PRESENTED IN **FANTASY CLASSICS**.

EDGAR ALLAN POE (page 1)

Edgar Allan Poe, the orphaned son of itinerant actors, led a tumultuous adolescence of drink and gambling, which resulted in the failure of both his university and military careers. Throughout his life he was plagued by poverty, poor health, insecurity, and depression, much by his own doing and a result of his continuing problems with alcohol. He struggled unsuccessfully as a writer until winning a short story contest in 1833. Poe's subsequent writing ranged from his rigorously metrical poetry to short stories, from journalism and distinguished literary criticism to the pseudo-scientific essays of *Eureka*. Today he is generally acknowledged as the inventor of both the gothic short story and the detective story, a pioneer of early science fiction and the founding father of the horror genre. He rightfully occupies the first volume in the *Graphic Classics* series, and stories by Edgar Allan Poe appear in:

Graphic Classics: Edgar Allan Poe
Horror Classics: Graphic Classics Volume Ten
Gothic Classics: Graphic Classics Volume Fourteen

ROD LOTT (page 1)

Oklahoma City resident Rod Lott is a freelance writer and graphic designer working in advertising and journalism. For twelve years, he has published and edited the more-or-less quarterly magazine *Hitch: The Journal of Pop Culture Absurdity* (www.hitchmagazine.com), and edits *Bookgasm*, a daily book review and news site at www.bookgasm.com. Rod's humorous essays have been published in several anthologies, including *May Contain Nuts* and *101 Damnations*. You can learn more about his work online at www.rodlott.com, and you can find more comics adaptations by Rod Lott in:

Graphic Classics: Edgar Allan Poe
Graphic Classics: Arthur Conan Doyle
Graphic Classics: H.G. Wells
Graphic Classics: H.P. Lovecraft
Graphic Classics: Jack London
Graphic Classics: Ambrose Bierce
Graphic Classics: O. Henry
Graphic Classics: Rafael Sabatini
Horror Classics: Graphic Classics Volume Ten
Adventure Classics: Graphic Classics Volume Twelve
Gothic Classics: Graphic Classics Volume Fourteen
Fantasy Classics: Graphic Classics Volume Fifteen

GERRY ALANGUILAN (cover, page 1)

Gerry Alanguilan has inked superhero comics for Marvel, DC and Image Comics on titles including *New X-Men Annual, Fantastic Four, Wolverine, X-Force, Superman: Birthright, Batman/Danger Girl, Silent Dragon* and many more. He retired from inking in December 2005 to concentrate on creating his own stories in the Philippines. To date, he has written and drawn *Wasted, Humanis Rex!, Dead Heart Stories, Johnny Balbona*, short stories for *Siglo: Passion* and *Siglo: Freedom*, and is currently working on *Timawa* (for *The Buzz Magasin*), *The Marvelous Adventures of The Amazing Dr. Rizal* (for *Fudge Magazine*), and *Elmer*, for his own Komikero Publishing.

More comics and illustrations by Gerry appear in:
Graphic Classics: H.P. Lovecraft
Graphic Classics: Bram Stoker
Graphic Classics: O. Henry
Graphic Classics: Rafael Sabatini

AMBROSE BIERCE (page 13)

Born in rural Ohio in 1842, Bierce became a printer's apprentice for a small Indiana newspaper until 1860, when he enlisted in the Union army and witnessed some of the major battles of the Civil War. Following a short military career, he resigned in disgust over a lack of promotion and instead pursued a successful career in journalism. In his time, Bierce was a celebrity as a satirical columnist, but disappointment over a lack of acceptance of his fiction and a troubled personal life caused him to become increasingly bitter and withdrawn in his later years. In 1913, at the age of 71, he crossed the border into Mexico, "with a pretty definite purpose, which, however, is not at present disclosable." He was never heard from again.

More stories by Ambrose Bierce are adapted in:
Graphic Classics: Ambrose Bierce
Horror Classics: Graphic Classics Volume Ten

MARK DANCEY (page 13)

Mark Dancey was born in Ann Arbor, Michigan in 1963. "For no good reason," Mr. Dancey co-founded the satirical and highly influential *Motorbooty Magazine* in the late 1980s and filled its pages with his comics and illustrations. In the 1990s and 2000s his work appeared "in many glossy consumer magazines and in the hep galleries of our most glamorous cities." Mark now lives in southwest Detroit, where he produces painstaking works in oil and prints posters under the aegis of his company, Iluminado. He is presently working on *Mythographic,* a volume of illustrated mythology. You are cordially invited to visit him at www.iluminado.us.

More comics and illustrations by Mark Dancey are in:
Graphic Classics: Ambrose Bierce
Graphic Classics: Mark Twain
Horror Classics: Graphic Classics Volume Ten

ARTHUR CONAN DOYLE (page 14)

Arthur Conan Doyle was born in 1859, studied in England and Germany and became a Doctor of Medicine at the University of Edinburgh. He built up a successful medical practice, but also wrote, and created his most famous character, Sherlock Holmes, in 1887. Following a less-successful practice as an oculist, Doyle concentrated on his writing career. He was proudest of his historical novels, such as *The White Company*, and in 1894 introduced his second popular character, Brigadier Gerard, and in 1912 a third, Professor Challenger. But Holmes continued to be his most famous creation. Doyle felt that Holmes was a distraction and kept him from writing the "better things" that would make him a "lasting name in English literature." He killed his detective in 1893 in *The Final Problem,* only to resurrect him in 1903 due to public demand. Doyle wrote an astonishing range of fiction including medical stories, sports stories, historical fiction, contemporary drama and verse. He also wrote nonfiction, including the six-volume *The British Campaign in France and Flanders.* His defense of British colonialism in South Africa led to his being knighted in 1902. By 1916 Doyle's investigations into Spiritualism had convinced him that he should rest the rest of his life to the advancement of the belief. He wrote and lectured on the Spiritualist cause until his death in 1930.

More stories by Arthur Conan Doyle appear in:
Graphic Classics: Arthur Conan Doyle
Adventure Classics: Graphic Classics Volume Twelve

ALEX BURROWS (page 14)

Journalist and writer Alex Burrows lives in Oxfordshire and works in London as Managing Editor for *Classic Rock* magazine. His publishing career began with *Arnie,* a comics and punk music zine which he co-published with artist Simon Gane. Alex's first adaptation for *Graphic Classics* was H.P. Lovecraft's *The Shadow Over Innsmouth* and *John Barrington Cowles* is his second. "I hadn't looked at the story before reading it for adaptation," says Alex, "and I was surprised because I was unaware of the occult literature that Conan Doyle wrote prior to his Sherlock Holmes work. It shows his breadth of scope and expertise. Maintaining the crucial suspense was the hardest part of the adaptation. But there was also the opportunity for producing some great scenes and locations — all done here exquisitely as usual by Simon. I love the bleak, unforgiving landscapes and climate of the UK's Scottish and Northern coastlines — Simon's artwork made me yearn for a remote mid-winter holiday break."

Alex and Simon's *The Shadow Over Innsmouth* is in:
Graphic Classics: H.P. Lovecraft

SIMON GANE (page 14)
British artist Simon lives and works in Bath. His first published strips appeared in the self-produced punk fanzine *Arnie*, and others followed in numerous mini comics. Recent titles include *All Flee*, a comic about a "finishing school for monsters" and *Paris*, penned by Andi Watson and released by SLG Publishing. He currently pencils the DC/Vertigo series *Vinyl Underground*. Examples of Simon's work can be found at www.simongane.com and in these other *Graphic Classics* volumes:

Graphic Classics: Arthur Conan Doyle
Graphic Classics: H.G. Wells
Graphic Classics: H.P. Lovecraft
Graphic Classics: Ambrose Bierce
Graphic Classics: Mark Twain
Graphic Classics: Robert Louis Stevenson

MARY SHELLEY (page 36)
Mary Wollstonecraft Godwin was the daughter of anarchist political writer William Godwin and feminist author Mary Wollstonecraft. She met poet Percy Bysshe Shelley when she was sixteen, and Shelley became a follower of her father's atheist philosophy. Mary eloped with the then-married Shelley in 1814, and bore him two children prior to the events retold in *Fantasmagoriana*, an original prologue to *Frankenstein* appearing in *Fantasy Classics*. In December 1816, shortly following the suicide of Shelley's first wife, the couple married and in 1818 *Frankenstein; or, The Modern Prometheus* first saw print. She authored a number of other novels, as well as short stories, biographies and travel books, but none approached the popular success of *Frankenstein*, which is adapted in:

Fantasy Classics: Graphic Classics Volume Fifteen

ANTONELLA CAPUTO (page 36)
Antonella was born and raised in Rome, Italy, and now lives in Lancaster, England. She has been an architect, archaeologist, art restorer, photographer, calligrapher, interior designer, theater designer, actress and theater director. Her first published work was *Casa Montesi*, a fortnightly comic strip which appeared in the national magazine *Il Giornalino*. She has since written comedies for children and scripts for comics and magazines in the UK, Europe and the U.S. She works with Nick Miller as the writing half of Team Sputnik, and has collaborated with Nick and other artists in:

Graphic Classics: Edgar Allan Poe
Graphic Classics: Arthur Conan Doyle
Graphic Classics: H.G. Wells
Graphic Classics: Jack London
Graphic Classics: Ambrose Bierce
Graphic Classics: Mark Twain
Graphic Classics: O. Henry
Graphic Classics: Rafael Sabatini
Horror Classics: Graphic Classics Volume Ten
Adventure Classics: Graphic Classics Volume Twelve
Gothic Classics: Graphic Classics Volume Fourteen
Fantasy Classics: Graphic Classics Volume Fifteen

ANNE TIMMONS (page 36, back cover)
Anne was born in Portland, and has a BFA from Oregon State University. In addition to her collaboration on the

Lulu Award-winning *GoGirl!* with Trina Robbins, Anne's work includes the Eisner Award-nominated *Dignifying Science* and the comics version of *Star Trek: Deep Space Nine*. She has also drawn and painted children's books, and covers and interior art for magazines including *Comic Book Artist* and *Wired*. In fall of 2008 her new book *Pigling*, a Korean Cinderella story, will be published by Lerner Books for their Graphic Myths collection. Anne's art from the anthology *9-11 Artists Respond* is now included in the Library of Congress Collection. More of her work can be seen at www.homepage.mac.com/tafrin, and her comics and illustrations appear in:

Graphic Classics: Jack London
Graphic Classics: Robert Louis Stevenson
Gothic Classics: Graphic Classics Volume Fourteen

LORD DUNSANY (page 58)
Lord Dunsany, born Edward John Moreton Drax Plunkett, wrote more than 70 books, beginning with *The Gods of Pegāna* in 1905. He is one of the most popular fantasy authors in the English language and was also a poet, a successful playwright, and a competitive chess player. *A Narrow Escape* first appeared in his 1916 collection *The Last Book of Wonder*. Dunsany died in Dublin in 1957. H. P. Lovecraft was a great admirer of his stories, and wrote of Dunsany: "To the truly imaginative he is a talisman and a key unlocking rich storehouses of dream."

Lord Dunsany's poem *After the Fire* is presented in:
Fantasy Classics: Graphic Classics Volume Fifteen

MILTON KNIGHT (page 58)
Milton Knight claims he started drawing, painting and creating his own attempts at comic books and animation at age two. "I've never formed a barrier between fine art and cartooning," says Milt. "Growing up, I treasured Chinese watercolors, Breughel, Charlie Brown and Terrytoons equally." His work has appeared in magazines including *Heavy Metal*, *High Times*, *National Lampoon* and *Nickelodeon Magazine*, and he has illustrated record covers, posters, candy packaging and T-shirts, and occasionally exhibited his paintings. Labor on *Ninja Turtles* comics allowed him to get up a grubstake to move to the West Coast in 1991, where he became an animator and director on *Felix the Cat* cartoons. Milt's comics titles include *Midnite the Rebel Skunk* and *Slug and Ginger*. His adaptation of Rafael Sabatini's *The Fool's Love Story* features characters from his long-running series *Hugo*, and more comics and illustrations by Milton Knight appear at www.miltonknight.net and in:

Graphic Classics: Edgar Allan Poe
Graphic Classics: H.G. Wells
Graphic Classics: Jack London
Graphic Classics: Ambrose Bierce
Graphic Classics: O. Henry
Graphic Classics: Rafael Sabatini
Horror Classics: Graphic Classics Volume Ten
Adventure Classics: Graphic Classics Volume Twelve

TOM POMPLUN
The designer, editor and publisher of *Graphic Classics*, Tom has a background in both fine and commercial art and a lifelong interest in comics. He designed and produced *Rosebud*, a journal of fiction, poetry and illustration, from 1993 to 2003, and in 2001 he founded *Graphic Classics*. Tom is currently working on a revised edition of *Graphic Classics: Ambrose Bierce*, scheduled for August 2008 release, and *Graphic Classics: Oscar Wilde*, for December 2008. The book will feature a new comics adaptation of *The Picture of Dorian Gray*, by British writer Alex Burrows and illustrated by *Graphic Classics* regular Lisa K. Weber, along with Wilde's play *Salome*, adapted by Tom and illustrated by Molly Kiely.